MIGLIARI

Time Pieces for Viola

Volume 2

c.1450 Chanson favorite d'Henri IV

Anon.

Fine

D.S. al Fine

AB 2817

1681 Hallelujah

from *O God, thou art my God*

Henry Purcell
(1659–1695)

AB 2817

1720 Recitativo and Arioso

from Sonata in E minor for viola da gamba

Georg Philipp Telemann
(1681–1767)

Andante drammatico

1762 Tambourin

François-Joseph Gossec
(1734–1829)

AB 2817

1791

Bei Männern, welche Liebe fühlen

from *The Magic Flute*

Wolfgang Amadeus Mozart
(1756–1791)

'Bei Männern, welche Liebe fühlen' (All men, who can feel love) is a famous duet for
soprano and baritone from Act 1 of the opera *Die Zauberflöte*, or *The Magic Flute*.

1817 The Trout

Op. 32, D. 550

Franz Schubert
(1797–1828)

AB 2817

*c.*1830 **La nouvelle carel**
(a cotillion dance)

Anon.

A popular dance of the 18th and 19th centuries, the 'cotillion' required dancers to move in geometric patterns, imitating the steps of a leading couple. It was commonly structured in two alternating parts.

1890 Gnossienne No. 1

Erik Satie
(1866–1925)

Très luisant
Shining

Questionnez
Questioning

Du bout de la pensée
At the tip of one's thoughts

Postulez en vous-même
Seek within yourself

Pas à pas
Step by step

Sur la langue
On the tip of the tongue

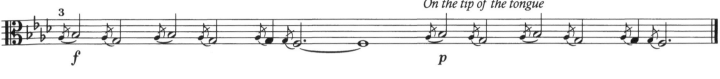

1896   The Crush Collision March

Scott Joplin
(1867/8–1917)

Tempo di marcia ♩ = 144

D.S. al Fine

1912 Pierrot's Serenade

from *Puppets, III*

Bohuslav Martinů
(1890–1959)

Scherzando (ma non troppo) ♩ = 184

1938 September Song

from *Knickerbocker Holiday*

Kurt Weill
(1900–1950)

1999 Landscape with Rumba

Philip Bass
(b. 1953)

Music origination by
Barnes Music Engraving Ltd, East Sussex

 9:14

Time Pieces
for Viola

VOLUME 2

Arranged by Philip Bass & Paul Harris

ABRSM

CONTENTS

Published by ABRSM (Publishing) Ltd, a wholly owned subsidiary of ABRSM
© 2002 by The Associated Board of the Royal Schools of Music

Time Pieces for Viola

Volume 2

*c.*1450 Chanson favorite d'Henri IV

Anon.

AB 2817

D.S. al Fine

1681 Hallelujah

from *O God, thou art my God*

Henry Purcell
(1659–1695)

1720 Recitativo and Arioso

from Sonata in E minor for viola da gamba

Georg Philipp Telemann
(1681–1767)

1762 Tambourin

François-Joseph Gossec
(1734–1829)

1791 Bei Männern, welche Liebe fühlen

Wolfgang Amadeus Mozart
(1756–1791)

from *The Magic Flute*

'Bei Männern, welche Liebe fühlen' (All men, who can feel love) is a famous duet for
soprano and baritone from Act 1 of the opera *Die Zauberflöte*, or *The Magic Flute*.

1817 The Trout

Op. 32, D. 550

Franz Schubert
(1797–1828)

c.1830 La nouvelle carel

(a cotillion dance)

Anon.

A popular dance of the 18th and 19th centuries, the 'cotillion' required dancers to move in geometric patterns, imitating the steps of a leading couple.
It was commonly structured in two alternating parts.

D.C. al Fine

1890 Gnossienne No. 1

Erik Satie
(1866–1925)

Du bout de la pensée

At the tip of one's thoughts

Postulez en vous-même
Seek within yourself

Pas à pas
Step by step

Sur la langue
On the tip of the tongue

1896   The Crush Collision March

Scott Joplin
(1867/8–1917)

Fine

D.S. al Fine

1912 Pierrot's Serenade

from *Puppets, III*

Bohuslav Martinů
(1890–1959)

Scherzando (ma non troppo) ♩ = 184

1938 September Song

from *Knickerbocker Holiday*

Kurt Weill
(1900–1950)

Moderato assai ♩ = 116

1999 Landscape with Rumba

Philip Bass
(b. 1953)

* 'cluster' chord played on the white notes of the keyboard; noteheads mark outer limits
† glissando with indefinite opening and closing pitch

Printed in England by Caligraving Ltd, Thetford, Norfolk

Music origination by
Barnes Music Engraving Ltd, East Sussex